MW01097993
LEMON
TASTY
THE LEMON IS
HERE, BABY!
10¢
BOUNCECASTLE
HAPPY
B-DAY
LOBBY
Los Secretos

Drexler lived with his Mom, Dad, and Queenie, his Sister.
He also lived with their dog, Bongo, who liked to tap a bongo with his tail when he heard music, and their old Aunt Lillan.

His mom was an underwater welder and was away from home a lot.
His Dad worked from home but was in his office a lot of the day,
so old Aunt Lillan watched Drexler and Queenie a lot.

Drexler loved his family, did well in school, and had great manners, saying "please" and "thank you" whenever he could. But there were also times when he would get into his share of trouble.

Like the time he dressed the refrigerator as a giant
and jousted with it using a broom,

Or the time his family rented a bouncy house for Queenie's birthday and it popped when he used it to create a shelter for all of the stray dogs and cats in the neighborhood,

Or the time he went into the living room to ask Aunt Lillan to get him a popsicle for lunch, but she was busy watching her favorite Spanish soap opera, "Los Secretos Del Desayuno," or in English, "The Secrets of Breakfast."

He tapped Aunt Lillan on the shoulder and asked, "May I please have a popsicle for lunch?"

Aunt Lillan turned around with the same stare she gave Drexler every time she had to pick up a refrigerator after a jousting match, or go into a deflated bouncy house to rescue 50 stray cats, and she said,

"Why don't you make a peanut butter and jelly sandwich and PRETEND it's a popsicle? Now, leave Aunt Lillan alone to watch her stories!" And she turned away slowly, mad that she had missed Juan putting way too much chili powder in his evil twin's scrambled eggs.

WONDROU
BREAD
PB

Drexler went to the kitchen, made a peanut butter and jelly sandwich, but couldn't find a popsicle stick. Wanting to do what Aunt Lillan said, he used the closest thing he could find – his finger. Drexler took a big bite, and you could hear him yell "OW!" all the way down the block.

While Aunt Lillan stayed hypnotized by the TV, watching workers on the ranch save animals from a cheesy queso flood, Drexler's dad, who heard the "OW!" from his office, came rushing into the kitchen to help Drexler.

Dad got the first aid kit and took care of Drexler's hurt finger.
"There you go, buddy. Just keep this bandage on it and your finger will be good as new. Next time you want a popsicle, please come see me instead of asking Aunt Lillan.
At least for a little while."

Drexler asked, "Are you sure I won't bug you when you're working, Dad?"
"It's ok," Dad answered. "I'd rather you knock on the door while I'm working than have you get hurt."

INSURANCE

Drexler was so used to Aunt Lillan giving him a stink-eye stare, so he was happy and surprised when Dad came to help him so quickly. He asked a question he had never asked Dad before. "Dad," he asked, "What do you do for work?"

Dad, finishing with Drexler's finger, looked up and proudly said, "I sell insurance."

Drexler looked puzzled and asked, "What is insurance?"

Dad began to explain, "Insurance is a service that is provided to people so that when something bad happens to them and they need help, we give them money that will make sure they are protected, especially when it involves something they have to pay for."

Drexler knew that when his family needed food they could go to the grocery store, or when they needed medicine they could go to the pharmacy to pick it up, but he couldn't picture something happening to someone that they couldn't pay for themselves. "What kind of something could happen to someone where they couldn't pay and they would need...insurance, Dad?" Drexler asked.

Dad thought and said, "There are all kinds of different reasons people might need insurance, and I sell many of those kinds so that we can be there to help when times get tough and someone doesn't expect it. There's homeowner's insurance for when there is unexpected damage to your house and the things in it," Dad said.

Drexler thought and asked, "If all of the stray cats in the bouncy house had homeowner's insurance, when it popped could they have bought a new blow-up shelter?"

Dad smiled and said, "That's the idea. It also works when certain things happen to things that you own. Remember when we were on vacation and had that hurricane warning at the hotel last summer? If your stuffed sloth, Sammy Sietsta, had been taken away by the hurricane, the kind of homeowners' insurance we have would help you get a new Sammy."

"Do you remember when the house your friend James lives in had the kitchen fire last year when his brother was making popcorn without his parents around?" Drexler remembered how sad his friend's family had been. "Well, they had a homeowner's insurance policy with me, and our company paid for them to stay in a hotel for a few nights while their house was being fixed."

Drexler said, "James was sad but had so much fun at the hotel and was so happy when he came home and his house was good as new!"

Dad replied, "That's what insurance is for, son."

"All drivers should have auto insurance," Dad added. "In most states it's the law. Auto insurance is there to help a driver when their car is damaged by mistake, like in a car accident."

"Like when I drove my Big Wheel through Aunt Lillan's pile of unmatched granny socks and ran over Queenie's California Christy car?"

"Yes," Dad said. "In that case you would have to pay Queenie from your auto insurance."

Drexler thought and said, "Hmm. Let's not tell Queenie aboutauto insurance yet."

"What other kinds of insurance are there?" Drexler asked.

"Well," Dad said, there is also insurance you might need if you start your own business, like..."

"Like my lemonade stand?" Drexler asked.

"Yes, like your lemonade stand," Dad answered. "There are a few different kinds of insurance you might need for a business, like Property insurance, in case you own the lemonade stand and something happens to it, like it's damaged in bad weather, or..."

"Or attacked by lemonade-craving raccoons?" Drexler asked.

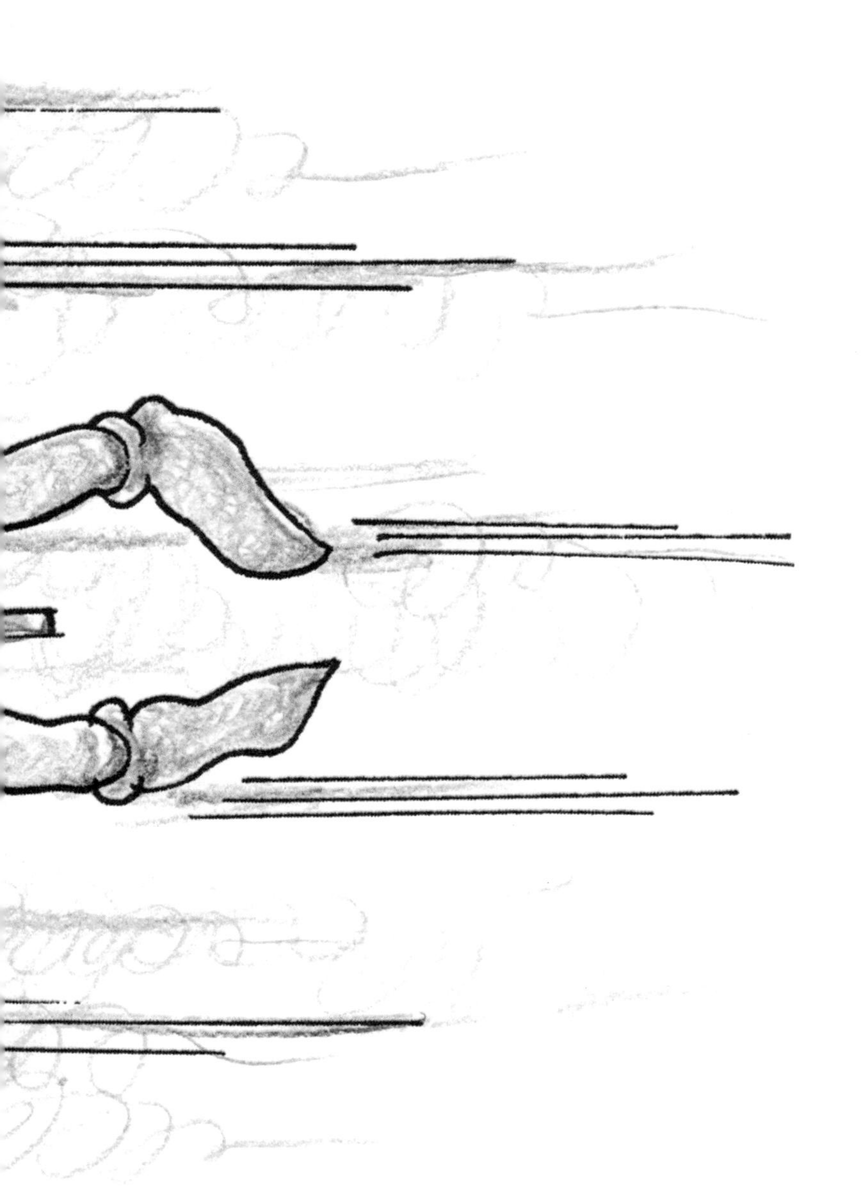

"That...or Liability, in case you..." Dad started, when Drexler asked, "Library-whattabee?" Drexler then imagined he and Queenie playing Frisbee with a library book.

"No, son, General Liability," dad sounded out. "Liability covers when the operations of the business cause some kind of damage to someone else. Like the time that really high wind caught your lemonade stand's umbrella and it hit Aunt Lillan, blowing her across the street," Dad whispered, "like a crazy, striped sock granny rocket."

Drexler asked, "Remember the time we were in the car and Bongo threw up on Aunt Lillan? Would we have needed both Auto and Pet insurance then?"

Dad laughed and said, "We were okay - well everyone except Aunt Lillan - wound up being ok, and we werent in an accident so we didn't need insurance for that. But if someone needs more than one kind of insurance we can always do what we call bundling, which is combining two different kinds of insurance so someone can pay a lower price a month for two."

Drexler said with pride, "Boy, Dad, I never knew you did something for work that helped so many people with so many things!"

Dad said, "Insurance makes a difference to people. I help people with their lives and with all kinds of needs that they have. You never asked me what I did before. Normally I would not have wanted you to bite your finger, but I'm glad we got a chance to talk."

Drexler started imagining himself enjoying the popsicle he had wanted in the first place and asked, “Dad, can I buy some Popsicle Insurance from you?”

Dad smiled and asked, “Drexler, what is Popsicle Insurance?”

“Well, if I eat a popsicle and get really bad brain freeze, will you ‘insure’ that the next time I want a popsicle you’ll still give me one? If I ask nicely?”

Drexler's stomach grumbled, and Dad said, "How about this: for Popsicle Insurance I will insure, or make sure, that after we make you a real peanut butter and jelly sandwich, I give you a real popsicle for dessert? It looks like your PB and J fell on the floor and I should make you a new one, anyway."

"Dad, I think Popsicle Insurance works for me. That would be great!" Drexler said. Drexler looked in the living room at Aunt Lillan and asked, "Dad, do you think we should make Aunt Lillan one?"

Dad looked and saw on the TV that the Mariachi band Juan's evil twin belonged to was in a breakfast food fight with Juan and that Aunt Lillan's attention was on her show. "Maybe tomorrow," Dad said, "Or as they say on Aunt Lillan's show, maybe mañana."

The End